THE SNOW BABY

THE SNOW BABY

Marie in Fur Costume

THE SNOW BABY

A TRUE STORY WITH TRUE PICTURES · By JOSEPHINE DIEBITSCH PEARY

NEW YORK · FREDERICK A. STOKES COMPANY · *PUBLISHERS*

7930

Dedicated to
" Her Grossmamma "

THE SNOW BABY

"A Wonderful Land of . . . Mountains, Glaciers, and Icebergs"

Hundreds and hundreds of miles away in the white frozen north, far beyond where the big ships go to hunt huge black whales, there is a wonderful land of snow and ice, mountains, glaciers, and icebergs; where strange little brown people called Eskimos, dressed all in the skins of animals, live in snow houses.

In summer in this wonderful land the sun never sets, but shines all the time day and night; the snow melts off the ground; blue and white and yellow flowers spring up; and soft-eyed, brown-coated reindeer wander about, cropping the short grass.

9

The ice breaks up and drifts out to sea; the glaciers or rivers of ice push forward, creaking and groaning, into the water, till enormous icebergs break off from them and float away like white ships. The blue waves dance and sparkle in the sun, and everywhere singing brooks rush down the mountains or fall in silvery cascades over the cliffs, where millions and millions of noisy seabirds come to lay their eggs.

Big black walrus, larger than oxen, crawl out upon the ice, and sleep in the sun, or fight with their long ivory tusks, and bellow till you can hear them miles away.

Glossy mottled seals swim in the water, and schools of narwhal,

"Live in Snow Houses"

" In Summer in this Wonderful Land "

which used to be called unicorns, dart from place to place faster than the fastest steam yacht; with their long white ivory horns, longer than a man is tall, flashing like spears in and out of the water.

Once in a while a fierce shaggy white bear goes running over the ice-cakes, or swimming through the water in search of a poor little seal on which to dine.

The Eskimos, paddling swiftly through the water in their strange skin boats, or kayaks, pursue all these animals, and kill them with harpoons and lances.

In winter there is no sun at all, and for four long, long months it is dark all the time, day and night, just as it is here in the night, only the moon and stars giving light. The ground is covered deep with snow, through which the poor deer have to dig with their hoofs for a few mouthfuls of grass and moss, the sea is covered with ice five or six feet thick, the birds have flown away, and the walrus and narwhal have gone far off to the open water. Only a few hungry bears and the Eskimos with their dogs are left; and the cold is so terrible that these would freeze to death in an hour if it were not for their thick warm fur coats, and the blanket of blubber underneath.

Far to the north of us, beyond the Arctic Circle,

" The Ice breaks up and drifts out to Sea "

" Big Ships that go to hunt Huge Whales"

lies a land inhabited by a little tribe of Eskimos, called Arctic Highlanders. These are the most northerly known people on the globe.

They are entirely dependent on their country for everything they need, and as it is very cold, and part of the year entirely without sunshine, there is very little plant life, and they live only upon the animals, using the meat for food and the skins for their clothing. During the short summer season when the sun shines, the grass

and flowers grow rapidly, the birds come back and build their nests, and, alas! the mosquitoes come forth in swarms. But this lasts only a short time.

Here in this wonderful land, in a little black house, under a great brown mountain, was found, one bright September day, a little snow-white baby girl with big blue eyes.

And such a funny house it was where she was found. It was only one story high, the outside was covered with thick, black tarred paper, the walls were more than a foot thick, and there were lots of windows for such a small house, one wide one running right across the top of the house, just like a hot-house.

" With their Long Ivory Tusks "

14

This was to enable the inmates to enjoy the sunshine just as long as it lasted.

All round the house was a close veranda, the walls of which were built of boxes of food, biscuits, sugar, coffee, and tea; for none of these things, in fact, nothing but meat could be bought in the country.

Inside the house the little room where the baby was found was lined with soft warm blankets, and there was a bright carpet on the floor, and lots of books, and a sewing-machine, and pictures on the walls. All these things, like the boxes of food outside, had been brought in the big ship which had brought the baby's father and mother to this strange country.

The bed on which the baby lay was covered with soft warm reindeer skins, through which even the terrible cold of the long dark night could not penetrate.

One window of the baby's room looked out upon a great glacier or river of ice, and the other upon high red and brown mountains surround-

" Walrus Larger than Oxen"

ing a bay in which floated lots and lots of icebergs, of the strangest and most fantastic shapes, so that you might easily imagine some of them to be the palace of the Frost King, others white ships, and in still others you might see the cruel white face of the Frost King himself.

When the strange people of the land heard that a baby had been found in this house, and that, wonderful to relate, this baby was perfectly white, they came — men, women, and children — hundreds of miles, riding upon sledges drawn by wild shaggy dogs, which looked like wolves, to see the little stranger.

These people are brown, with

" White Ivory Horns Longer than a Man is Tall"

16

black shaggy hair, and dress entirely in furs both summer and winter.

They said "OW-NAY'" and "AH-NAN-NAN" to her, at which she stared with wide-open eyes; and then they wanted to touch her to see if

" Eskimos in their Strange Skin Boats "

she was warm and not made of snow, she was so white.

And if by chance she happened to smile when looking at one of them, then there was great rejoicing, for this was counted very lucky.

So they called her "AH'-POO-MIK'-A-NIN-NY (the Snow Baby), and brought her presents

of fur mittens, little sealskin boots, walrus tusks, baby bear and seal skins, and many other things.

It was near the end of the Snowland summer when the baby was born, and six weeks afterwards the sun went away to be gone all through the long winter night of four months.

Just before he went baby was taken for her first outing. It was very, very cold, the thermometer far below the freezing-point, and the ground was covered deep with snow; but baby was tucked into a little reindeer-skin bag, which covered her completely all except her head. This was covered with a little foxskin hood; then baby, bag, and all were wrapped in the stars and stripes, and taken out of doors.

" Wrapped in the Stars and Stripes "

18

Ahnighito's Birthplace — " Such a Funny House it was "

Then the sun went away, and for days and weeks baby lived in the little room where a lamp was burning night and day.

Here she had her daily bath, and slept and crowed at the lamp and the pictures on the wall, and grew bigger and whiter every day. How she did enjoy these baths after she got to be a little older, when her mother closed every door in the room, put an oil stove inside the bed curtains which were drawn close, then sponged the baby with warm water, and after she was dry let her roll for a little while in the pile of soft warm bear and deer skins on the bed.

19

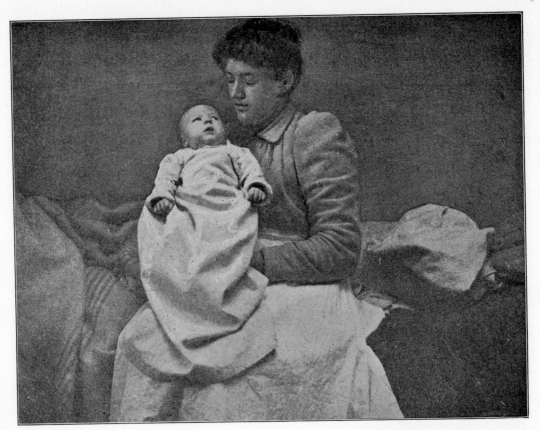

" A Little Snow White-Baby Girl with Big Blue Eyes "

Her Eskimo friends kept coming to see her whenever they could, though they did not always come in to the room, as they were not very clean.

After a long, long time the terrible night began to draw to an end, and every clear day at noon there was an hour or two of daylight.

It was decided that when the sun did return, no matter how cold it might be, baby was to go out

Bed on which Baby Lived

every day, so one of the Eskimo women was busy making a little Eskimo suit for her, all of furs.

There were only two pieces in this suit, — a little hooded coat, and a pair of little trousers and boots in one.

Boys and girls, and men and women, all wear trousers in this Snowland.

The softest and warmest fox and baby-deer skins were selected for these clothes. The little trousers or nannookies were made with the fur on the outside, and reached from her waist, where

21

they were fastened with a draw-string to her ankles, where a fur boot made of the same warm deer-skin, but with the fur on the inside, next the foot, was sewed to each leg, thus making it impossible for the cold air to get to her little feet and legs.

The kapetah, or foxskin coat, was after the same pattern as your sweaters, that is, without any open-ing down the front or back, and to the neck was sewed a round hood, the opening made to just fit about her little face. This coat her mother pulled on over baby's head and well down over her nan-nookies, so that here too no cold air could chill the little girl.

About the wrists and around the face open-ing of the hood, fox-tails were sewed, which helped very much to keep her face and hands

" They were not very Clean "

22

" There were only two Pieces in this Suit "

warm. This costume was made by a woman named AH-NI-GHI´-TO; so, when the baby was christened, she too was called AH-NI-GHI´-TO. She was also named Marie for her only aunt, who was waiting in the far-off home land to greet her little niece.

23

At last, one day about the middle of February, the great yellow sun popped up above the tops of the mountains and covered everything with the brightest sunlight.

Little AH-NI-GHÍ-TO was asleep when the sun first looked into the room, but in a few minutes she woke up, and as the room had been specially warmed to give her a sun bath, her mother took her out of her little nest and placed her, all white and naked, in the sunlight on the bed.

How the big blue eyes did open at the strange sight. How she laughed and jumped and stretched her little hands out in the yellow light, just as if she was bathing in perfumed golden water. It was the first time she had ever seen the sun.

After this, every sun-shiny day she had her sun bath, when she

" Stretched her Little Hands out in the Yellow Light "

would try to seize the sunbeams slanting through the room, and failing in this would try to pick up bits of sunlight on the bed.

On every pleasant day she was dressed in her little fur suit, tucked into her deerskin bag, and carried out.

Do you know how the tulip and hyacinth and narcissus bulbs grow and blossom after they are brought out of the cold, dark cellar into the warm, sunny window?

25

" Some Dogs were bought for Her "

Well, little AH-NI-GHI'-TO was just a little human bulb that had been kept in the cold and dark for five months and now was brought out into the bright sunlight; and she grew like a tulip, and her eyes grew brighter and bluer, and her cheeks were like "Jack" roses. So rapidly did she grow that very soon she was too heavy for mother to carry.

Then some dogs and a little Eskimo sledge were bought for her, with a knife and some biscuit and coffee, and a snug little box, just large enough

26

for her to sit in, fastened on the sledge.   After that
AH-NI-GHI'-TO had a sleigh-ride every day.
You should have seen her team, with their bright
eyes, sharp pointed ears, and big bushy tails.
There was "Lassie," and "Lady," and sometimes
steady old black Panikpah, who had been far to the
north here, across the "great ice," and had eaten
musk-ox meat.

Sometimes they would walk along with heads
and tails up, every now and then looking round at
the baby.

Then at the crack of the whip they would dash
off at a gallop, with the driver running beside the
sledge and guiding it past the rocks and lumps of
ice.

But they always seemed to understand that they
were drawing a little baby, for they never attempted
to run away, as they often did with their Eskimo
masters.

It was very, very cold now, colder even than
during the long winter night; but, wrapped up in
her warm furs, little AH-NI-GHI'-TO did not
feel it.

" The Women kissed her Hands'

A great many of the natives came to see the little white girl. The women kissed her hands, and she made friends with all the queer little brown babies sticking their heads out of their mothers' hoods, for the Eskimo babies have no cradles or anything of the kind, but are just carried all the time by their mothers in great fur hoods on their backs.

28

Soon AH-NI-GHI'-TO began to talk Eskimo, and would say "Ta'koo" (look), "Atu'do" (more), and she never said yes and no, but "Ah'-py" and "Nag'-ga."

Then she had a playmate, a little Eskimo boy about five or six years old, whose father had been killed by a savage walrus which he had harpooned and which had dragged him into the water and drowned him. His mother, too, was dead.

His name was Nip-San-Gwah, though every one called him Kood-Look'-Too, which means "the little orphan boy."

He was very fond of AH-NI-GHI'-TO and would try to follow her when she went in her sledge. How queer he

Kood-Look'-Too

29

looked with his little round fat face, bright black eyes, and little short bearskin trousers. Then he would make little snow igloos, or houses, for her, just like the one his father and mother had lived in, and would get a whip and try to show her how he would drive her dogs for her after he got a little larger.

Sometimes Kood-Look´-Too would make believe he was a white boy, and would dress himself up in cast-off clothes, to look, as he thought, like such a boy.

Whether he succeeded or not you can see for yourself in the picture.

And E-Klay-I-Shoo — or "Miss Bill," as she was called — must not be forgotten.

She was an Eskimo girl, about twelve years old, who used to take care of AH-NI-GHI´-TO.

"Made believe he was a White Boy"

" Miss Bill "

"Miss Bill" never had a dress or a hat in her life, but dressed in a seal-skin coat, short foxskin trousers, or nannookies, and long-legged kamiks, or sealskin boots. She and Kood-Look'-Too and her father Nook-Tal, with the rest of the family, lived in a small round tent, or tupic, of sealskins, with big stones all around the edge of it, to keep the wind from blowing it away.

The sun kept getting higher in the sky and warmer every day, till finally it did not set at all day or night, the snow was melting, and the rocks and ground getting dry.

" A Tupic of Sealskin "

"In her Gray Gown she looked like a Little Monk"

Such a good time as AH-NI-GHI'-TO had now. Her furs were put away, and in thick, warm woollen gowns, with a sunbonnet to protect her tender face——for even up here the sun and wind in summer may burn the skin——she was out doors nearly all the time. She could creep and roll about a little now, and she had so much to do.

There was the gravel slope back of the house, in which to search for pretty round red and white pebbles. As she rolled about over this in her gray gown, she looked like a little monk.

32

" There were Lots of Little Puppies to feed and play with "

There were lots of little puppies to feed and play with, such plump, round, soft, playful little puppies, you could not believe that when they grew up, they would be great, strong dogs, who could draw their masters on a sledge forty and fifty miles in a day, and even fight the great white polar bear.

There was Hector, the big St. Bernard, who would come to have his head patted by the baby.

3

33

" Hector, the big St. Bernard "

She was a little afraid of Hector, however, he was so big and strong, and rough in his playfulness.

Finally, there were the flowers, yellow and purple and white, which must be picked and played with.

" To be picked and played with "

" She rolled about, tossing the Bright Pebbles "

Days when there was not a bit of wind, and the sun was shining brightly, AH-NI-GHI´-TO took her sun bath out of doors. A deerskin was spread on the gravel, to keep the sharp stones from hurting the tender little limbs, and on this, with all her clothes taken off, she rolled about, tossing the bright pebbles and talking to the sun, the puppies, and the

35

" Baby Lake, a Beautiful Little Pond"

flowers, till her skin was rosy as the morning. So all through the summer months — June, July, and well into August — AH-NI-GHI'-TO passed the sunny days.

Sometimes she was taken to Baby Lake, a beautiful little pond that lay in the valley, a few hundred yards back of the house, and from which a murmuring brook ran through moss and over rocks, down to the head of the bay.

And during her sun baths she must have absorbed the bright summer sunlight, for never was there a happier, sunnier-tempered, more smiling baby than she.

Ah-ni-ghi´-to and her Mother

At last, one day late in August, the same big black ship which had brought AH-NI-GHI´-TO'S father and mother to the Snowland, came up the bay, forcing her way through the ice and throwing it in every direction, just the way a snow-plough drives through a big drift, and stopped just in front of the house.

Then AH-NI-GHI´-TO and her mother took "Bill" and some of the puppies on board the ship, and it steamed away south again, to bring AH-NI-GHI-TO to her grandmothers and aunt, who had never seen her.

When "Miss Bill" left her Snowland to come to the

" The Ship steamed away "

United States with AH-NI-GHI′-TO and her mother, she left her father and mother and two sisters, who were very proud to have her go to the land of the white man, and see the animals and trees and houses and people whose pictures they had seen in magazines.

In a year, when the ship returned for AH-NI-GHI′-TO'S father, "Miss Bill" would come back and tell her people all about the strange things she had seen.

By the time Philadelphia was reached, AH-NI-GHI′-TO had begun to talk, and called "Miss Bill" "Billy-Bah." By this name she is known among her people to-day. "Billy-Bah" was about twelve years old, and never in her life had she seen a

Ahtungahnaksoah

38

" Then the Sun went away "

house larger than the little one-story black house where the stork brought AH-NI-GHÍ-TO as a baby; never had she seen a bush or a tree, and never a horse or a cow, a wagon or a carriage, a train of cars or a steam-engine.

She had never had a bath until AH-NI-GHÍ-TO'S mother gave her one on board ship, and she could not understand why she must wash herself and brush her hair every morning.

On reaching Philadelphia, AH-NI-GHÍ-TO, with her mother and " Billy-Bah," drove to the railroad station, and "Billy-Bah's" eyes nearly danced out of her head, at the sight of what she called the big dogs (horses) which pulled the carriage, and the high igloos (Eskimo houses) that lined the streets. The station, she said, was the largest and finest igloo she had ever seen, and she was loath to leave it. When she saw an engine pull out a train of cars, she clung to AH-NI-GHI´-TO'S mother and asked what sort of an animal it was, and would it eat people. Long after the train which was taking the little party to AH-NI-GHI´-TO'S grandmother and aunt had started, "Billy-Bah" sat with both hands clutching the seat in front of her, and gazed in amazement at the trees and fences which seemed to fly past.

This little dusky maiden, who was the youngest of her people to reach the land of sunshine and plenty, had everything to learn, just the same as AH-NI-GHI´-TO.

First, she must learn to talk, for of course she could not speak English; then she must learn to eat, for in the Snowland her people eat nothing but meat.

THE SNOW BABY

She must learn that meals were served at regular times, that we bathed daily, and retired and arose at given times.

All this was new to her, for in her country the people eat whenever they are hungry. They have no tables or chairs, and never prepare meals. Sometimes, when it is very cold, they will cut slices off the chunks of frozen meat which are lying about on the floors of their igloos, and steep them in water heated over their lamps.

When they are sleepy, they curl up anywhere and go to sleep. Bathing was unknown to them until they saw AH-NI-GHI´-TO'S father and mother; indeed, they never even washed their faces, but perhaps this was because water is very scarce during the greater part of the year. Everything is frozen, and their only fire and light is what they get from their ikkimer (lamp).

This ikkimer, or lamp, is a shallow stone dish, on the centre of which are heaped pieces of

blubber (fat), and across the front edge is placed dried moss. This moss acts as a wick, and as the fat melts it is absorbed by the moss, and this is lit with flint and steel. This is the only heat and light that is to be found in an Eskimo hut at any time.

Billy-Bah has had to learn by sad experience that she could not put her toys down anywhere in the streets of Washington and find them again hours afterward, as she could do in her own country.

When Santa Claus visited AH-NI-GHI'-TO, he also visited Billy-Bah for the first time in her life. He brought her many toys and also useful things.

She was pleased with the Christmas tree and with AH-NI-GHI'-TO'S toys, but did not seem to care for hers at all, hardly looking at them. But when she was told it was time for her to go to bed, she asked if she might take all of her presents to her room; permission was given, and she

trotted off, making three trips before she had all her things safely upstairs. An hour later AH-NI-GHÍ-TO'S mother noticed a bright light in Billy-Bah's room, and on opening the door she beheld the little Eskimo seated on the floor with all her treasures about her, celebrating her first Christmas.

She took great pleasure in sewing for her doll, and whenever anything was made for AH-NI-GHÍ-TO, Billy-Bah would make the same for her doll. By the time she returned to her home she was quite a little seamstress.

Her trunk was a regular Noah's Ark. A bit of everything that was given her during her stay was always carefully put into it, to be carried back home and explained to her friends.

In July it was decided the great ship should sail to the land of the midnight sun to bring AH-NI-GHÍ-TO'S father home, and Billy-Bah would return to her family.

" Riding with Eskimo Bear-Hunters"

She was very happy at the thought of home, but wished AH-NI-GHI'-TO might go too.

When she reached the Snowland, there was great rejoicing among her people, and feasts were given of fine raw walrus, seal, and bear meat, in honor of the young member of the tribe who had seen the sun rise and set every day for a whole year.

About two hours after landing, Billy-Bah was seen with a piece of meat weighing about five pounds, enjoying her first meal in a year.

While AH-NI-GHI'-TO'S father remained behind in the Snowland, one day after he had been riding on his sledge for days with some of his Eskimo bear-hunters, he came to a mountain,

" The Great Brown Woman "

where he found a great piece of brown iron which many years ago had fallen from the sky and from which the Eskimos had made their knives.

The Eskimos called this piece of iron a woman, because their great-grandfathers had told them that *their* great-grandfathers had said that when it first fell from the sky it looked like a great brown woman. Now so much of it had been pounded off for knives that its shape was gone, but the Eskimos believed that the spirit of the woman still remained. Near by was a smaller

"Were hauled over Rocks and Snow"

piece of iron which had been her dog some-
where up among the stars.

These great pieces of iron were so wonderful
that AH-NI-GHI'-TO'S father thought he would

like to take them back
to America, where every
one might see them;
so when the ship came
back after him the
brown woman and her
dog were hauled over
the rocks and snow and
ice to the ship, and

"A Smaller Piece which had been her Dog"

46

hoisted on board.   When AH-NI-GHI′-TO'S father had brought home the two heaven-born stones, the woman and the dog, he told several scientific gentlemen in New York that there still remained in the Snowland another and much larger stone which had fallen from the sky together with the woman and her dog.   This the natives call the woman's tupic, or tent.   These gentlemen called the stones meteorites, and were very anxious to have the largest one also.

So in 1897 AH-NI-GHI′-TO, with her father and mother and her good colored nurse Laura, boarded the ship and sailed for the Snowland to bring home the last of the stones.

AH-NI-GHI′-TO was now nearly four years old, and looked forward with pleasure to seeing the Snowland and all the queer little brown people again.

On the way north AH-NI-GHI′-TO, who was not seasick, enjoyed the brisk cool wind, and never tired of the beautiful icebergs which floated past.   A stop was made at Godhavn in South Greenland to get a supply of drinking water.

Marie

Here the natives are almost like white people. They have been living with the Danish families who occupy this part of Greenland for such a long time that they have become quite civilized both in looks and manners.

The Danes compel them to go to school and also to church; in this way they are growing more knowing every day.

They had seen AH-NI-GHI'-TO when she

" On the Way North "

and her mother came from the Snowland three years ago and AH-NI-GHI´-TO was only one year old; now they were anxious to see her again, and crowded to the ship, bringing her all sorts of presents and receiving others in return.

The nurse Laura was the first colored woman these natives had ever seen, and they thought her a great curiosity.   She was invited everywhere with AH-NI-GHI´-TO, but Laura was afraid to accept anything from these queer-looking people until AH-NI-GHI´-TO and her

49

mother went with her and she found how kind every one was and anxious to please her.

It happened that there were no Danish children in this place, but many little Eskimos, all eager to see AH-NI-GHI'-TO'S doll and to play with her. Only a few hours were spent here, and then AH-NI-GHI'-TO and Laura were brought to the vessel in a little boat and the great ship pushed toward the north again.

The sun did not set at all now, and at any time AH-NI-GHI'-TO could see his big face shining down upon her. This was very pleasant, for although it was quite cold AH-NI-GHI'-TO, wrapped in her furs, spent most of her time on deck watching the gulls that were circling about the ship, and the seals that kept popping up their black heads to gaze in open-eyed astonishment at the big black ship that came rushing through the water toward them. These seals are funny little creatures, so full of curiosity that when they see anything coming toward them they keep their heads above water until the object is close to them; then they quickly dive, but come up again at a safer distance to resume their gazing. They are often harpooned by the natives, who fasten a white sail across the front of the kayak (skin boat) in such a way as to make it look as if a white piece of ice were floating along. In this sail a tiny hole is made through which the hunter watches his chance. The seal's curiosity gets the best of him, and he does not dive in time to dodge the harpoon which is thrown from behind the white cloth. The Eskimos are very fond of seal meat, and the skins are used for their clothing.

AH-NI-GHI-'TO thought it very strange to have bedtime come when the sun was shining brightly. She declared it would be quite impossible to sleep at night if there was no night; so her

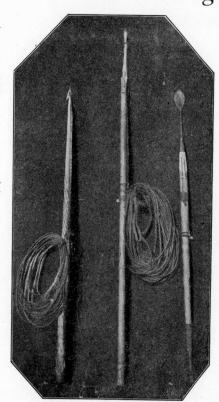

Harpoons and Lances

51

mother made night for her in their little state-room by taking a big soft felt hat belonging to her father and pushing it into the port hole through which the light came. AH-NI-GHÍ-TO was now quite satisfied, and slept soundly until break-fast time. When it was time to rise, the hat was pulled out, and lo! the room was flooded with sunlight. In a little while AH-NI-GHÍ-TO would call, "Mother, it is daylight, time to get up."

A bright fire was kept burning in the cabin, and Laura thought it wonderful that she should be quite comfortable beside a fire in midsummer; but when she awoke one morning and found it snowing hard, she said this was surely the most extraordinary thing she had ever known. Snow in August! "Why, if I tell this to my home folks, they won't believe me, but will think I am joking," she said.

Finally the Snowland was reached, and the Eskimos were wild with joy when they caught sight of the ship, for they all loved AH-NI-GHÍ-TO'S father, and knew he had brought them

" It is no Wonder the Snow Baby is so Tall"

many useful presents. All wanted to see AH-NI-GHI´-TO, and the women were particularly anxious to see how much she had grown, and if she still looked so white. One woman brought her baby, a wee boy, whose birthday was the same as AH-NI-GHI´-TO'S, to compare the children. When she saw how much larger AH-NI-GHI´-TO was than her boy, she smilingly stepped up beside AH-NI-GHI´-TO'S mother and showed how much taller the American woman was than

53

" Another Boat-load of Eskimos came aboard"

she, and pointing to AH-NI-GHI´-TO'S tall father, said: "It is no wonder the Snow Baby is so tall." Another boat-load of Eskimos just then came aboard, and who should be among them but "Billy-Bah"? How glad she was to see AH-NI-GHI´-TO, and how much she had to tell her. She did not want to stay on deck where the others were, but asked if she might go down in the cabin with AH-NI-GHI´-TO. Once away from

54

her people "Billy-Bah" talked English with AH-NI-GHI-TO, about the people she had known at AH-NI-GHI'-TO'S home; she asked how Hector the big St. Bernard dog was, and if AH-NI-GHI'-TO still had the little kitty "Billy-Bah" used to take to bed every night. Then they played with the dolls and looked at the picture books together. "Billy-Bah" gave AH-NI-GHI'-TO a number of ivory figures of men, women, dogs, bears, walrus, and seals, which she had carved from the teeth of walrus.

AH-NI-GHI'-TO'S father now had several barrels of ship's biscuit taken ashore, to be distributed among the natives. Everyone on board was anxious to get ashore, that he might get his share. "Billy-Bah" had been told that AH-NI-GHI'-TO would give her biscuit and tea and sugar, so she was content to remain in the cabin. Only one man refused to go, when he was told if he did not go he would not get any biscuit. Upon talking with him it was learned that he was "Billy-Bah's" husband, and he was afraid the ship

might sail away with his wife and without him, if he went ashore. AH-NI-GHI'-TO'S father assured him this would not be the case, and he speedily followed the others in the boats.

"Billy-Bah's" husband was very proud of his wife, for besides having travelled to the white man's country and seen wonderful things, she was one of the best seamstresses in the tribe, and kept her husband's clothing, as well as her own, in good order, though she was now only fifteen years old. But AH-NI-GHI'-TO was sorry to see that she kept herself just as dirty as her companions. It seemed as though she thought she had bathed enough, while in AH-NI-GHI'-TO'S home, to last her during her lifetime.

After AH-NI-GHI'-TO'S father had selected the Eskimos who were to help him move the great heaven-born stone, the old ship turned her nose toward Meteorite Island, where this mass of iron lay. It was snowing so thick and fast that one could not see any distance ahead, and

AH-NI-GHI´-TO thought she must be sailing through the clouds, because, when she looked beyond the ship, she could see nothing but whirling snow-flakes above, below, and all about her. The ship moved along very slowly, feeling her way carefully, to avoid collision with the floating icebergs, numbers of which were to be seen before the snow descended. At last the island was safely reached, and AH-NI-GHI´-TO'S father, with the help of the Eskimos, at once began his search for the great meteorite. Everything was now buried under the snow, which was still falling fast. The great iron rock was soon found, however, and the snow removed; then the work of getting it alongside the ship was begun. This was no easy thing, for it was found to weigh nearly one hundred tons.

For a week everybody worked. The Eskimos, with AH-NI-GHI´-TO'S father to lead them, worked by night, — for you know it was daylight all the time, even when the sun was behind the clouds, — and the captain of the ship, with his men, worked during the day.

The great iron stone was shaped like one of the Eskimo tents, and for that reason the natives called it "tupic." They chatted all the time they were at work, wondering what the woman could have done that she should have been cast out of the sky with her dog and her tent. "Billy-Bah" told AH-NI-GHI´-TO that she had heard her great-grandfather say that his grandfather told him when these stones first fell from the heavens they were red-hot, but after they had cooled, they looked just like other rocks about them, and none of his people thought they were any different, until one day one of the dusky hunters of the tribe had shot his last arrow into a polar bear, and the animal, though wounded, had managed to escape, leaving the hunter without any arrows.

He hastened to the shore, and began looking for sharp stones from which to make new arrow-heads. As he came upon the heaven-born stones, it occurred to him that perhaps these would give him luck, and picking up a large stone, he began to pound down upon one of the sharp brown ridges of the iron stone. Wherever he struck the brown coat became spotted with silver, but instead of knocking off a splinter, the stone with which he struck flew into fragments. He then searched far and near for a piece of rock harder than the one he had been using, and after a long time he found a piece. Hurrying again to the meteorite, he began to pound and chip, and to his joy he saw that he was making an impression on the iron stone. After hours and hours of hard work, he succeeded in getting off a splinter. How it glittered in the sunlight; and when he ran his finger over the edge, the spurting blood taught him how sharp it was.

This was more than he had hoped for; if it cut his finger by simply passing it over the edge, how much more apt would it be to cut into an animal when it was sent from the bow! On and on he worked, until he had enough splinters or scales to make the arrow-head; then forth he went to try his luck. Not an animal escaped. Just as sure as he struck a bear, or a fox, or a seal, with the arrow, just so sure the animal was his; and the more he used the arrow the sharper it became, until the thought came to him that this iron stone would make better knives than those of stone and ivory which his people now used, if he could only succeed in getting the pieces off.

He returned to his people, and told them of the good luck the heaven-born stone had brought him, and then he showed them the bright, sharp arrow-head, and they all agreed that good knives could be made of this iron stone. Then all the natives of this village set out at once, and travelled many miles, until they came to the front of a great river of ice called a glacier. This great ice stream comes creeping slowly down the mountain side, and pushes in front of it great heaps of stones and dirt. From among these stones the natives selected the hard smooth cobbles of what we call trap-rock, but which they knew only as very hard stones.

Loading their sledges with their tents and as many of these stones as they could carry, they travelled over the snow and ice to Meteorite Island. Here they camped, and while the women put up the tents, and got them ready, the men

" Then for the Hunt"

cleared away the snow from the stones and began to work. For many "sleeps," as the Eskimos say, they pounded and hammered and worked, until they had fashioned a few arrow-heads and also some rude knives. Then for the hunt, which lasted a week. They could hardly believe their eyes, when at the end of that time they saw the number of slaughtered animals,— more than had ever before fallen to their lot in a whole season. Nearly all the hunters would be able to have new

61

" Dogs that could draw their Masters on a Sledge "

fur clothing, and every family would have a new, soft, warm deerskin for the bed.

The Eskimos living hundreds of miles up the coast from here heard of the wonderful arrows and knives made from the heaven-sent stones; but as they did not have dogs and sledges enough to bring all the hunters and their families down where the stones lay, half a dozen of the strongest men took the best dogs and sleds and started for the iron mountain, promising to bring back a piece of the iron large enough to make knives and arrow-heads for all. First they stopped at one of the great glaciers, and gathered a sledge-load of the trap rocks; then on they went to Meteorite Island. They were delighted with the knives and arrow-heads which their friends proudly brought forth, and when they were told how deadly the arrow-head was, and shown the pile of meat procured in the hunt, they could wait to hear no more, but hurried over to the iron woman, eager to begin their work. By working steadily, they were able to secure enough scales of the metal to tip their arrow-heads and make their knives, but it seemed impossible to pound off the large piece which they had promised to bring back with them. Long and patiently they worked, chipping and pounding day after day, while the returning sun kept getting higher in the sky, the days grew longer, and the air warmer. The great sheet of snow-covered sea-ice over which the hunters had driven their dogs and sledges was beginning to soften under the caresses of the summer sun. Pools of water began to collect like cool green shadows on the white rolling surface, while numerous black specks on the white sheet showed where sleeping

A Short Rest

seals were sunning themselves beside their front doors, which opened into the deep sea. Soon the ice would break up and move out, and then the hunters could not return to their families until the Arctic winter set in again, which would not be for three or four months. This idea did not please them, so they redoubled their efforts to break off the large lump upon which they had been working; and just as they were about to give up, the head of the iron woman came off. This head must have weighed five hundred pounds, and would supply the people up the coast with all the iron they would need for arrows and knives for a long while. The precious package

Homeward Bound

was carefully done up in sealskins, and placed on one of the sledges, and two of the hunters rode beside it, to take care that it did not slide off, and also to drive the dogs, ten of the finest and strongest animals in the pack. The other sledges were loaded with the meat and furs of the animals which had been killed during their stay at the island, and then the little party joyfully started for home.

They found the ice very rotten in places, and often it was covered four or five inches deep with water, through which the dogs had almost to swim and pull the sledges. While crossing one of these

65

places, the dogs drawing the sledge on which the treasured iron lay, suddenly broke through the ice. For a brief moment they struggled to get a foothold amid the broken ice, yelping pitifully with terror, but in the next instant the sledge with its heavy load of men and iron came crashing among them, and shot beneath the water, carrying men and iron and dogs with it. The force and weight of the sledge must have carried it under the unbroken ice, for neither men nor dogs were seen again.

This the natives considered the punishment of the spirit of the iron woman for destroying the stone, and from that time to the present it has been looked upon as bad luck to try to move either of the stones.

It was for this reason that the Eskimos warned AH-NI-GHI'-TO'S father, when he told them he would take the wonderful stones to his country, not to touch them, for something dreadful would surely happen to him. When they found he was determined, nevertheless, to take away the meteorites, they helped him loosen them and take them

Ah-ni-ghi'-to and One of her Brown Fur-clad Friends

down to the ship, but refused to assist him in putting them on board.

While the work of getting the iron tent alongside the ship was going on, AH-NI-GHI'-TO had a merry time. After the sun shone again, the snow melted rapidly, and she spent her time on shore, picking flowers and berries, which grew among the rocks and on the hillsides; and the Eskimo women built her play "igloos" (houses) just like their own, and taught her different games which she and Laura played with the brown fur-clad children of the North.

After many days the iron tupic was ready to be put on board. Everything in the ship had been stowed, and the ship's hold filled with rocks, on which the iron stone should rest.

AH-NI-GHI´-TO'S father had built a bridge from the shore to the middle of the ship, where a big opening in the deck, called the hatch, gave an entrance for the big stone to the hold of the ship. This bridge was built of great oak timbers as long as a tree is tall, and on top of the timbers a railroad track was laid. When the iron stone was dug from the frozen bed in which it had lain so long, it was lifted high enough to slip under it a heavy sled of strong oak timbers, bolted together with long iron bolts and shod with iron.

To lift so heavy a mass of iron,—for the tupic weighed nearly one hundred tons,—powerful machines called jacks were used, and with their assistance, too, the great sledge with its heavy load was pushed on to the end of the bridge. The rails were smeared with grease, and strong ropes fastened from the steam-engine to the sledge to help pull, while the powerful jacks pushed. The meteorite was chained down to the sledge with heavy chains and then covered over with a big American flag. AH-NI-GHI'-TO was now told that she must christen the big brown stone with a bottle of wine as soon as it began to move. So she stood with her father just behind the car, when the signal was given to start. Her mother and the Captain began to pump at the jacks, the engine snorted, the ropes straightened, and the big bridge began to groan and creak. It seemed as if nothing could make the meteorite leave its home; but at last a great shout from the men told that the sledge was slowly moving, and then crash went the wine-bottle, and "I name thee AH-NI-GHI'-TO," said the little godmother.

Having once started, the great stone moved slowly and steadily along the greased track, until it rested over the open hatch. Then the men gave three cheers for AH-NI-GHI´-TO, the little godmother, and three more for her father, who had overcome all the obstacles and at last succeeded in getting the largest known meteorite safely on board.

The Eskimos stood on shore and watched everything with the greatest interest, but they could not be persuaded to come on board ship. They felt very sure the vessel would sink and all be lost, as were the men, sledge, and dogs that were taking away the iron woman's head.

It required a few more days of labor to get the unwilling monster into the hold of the ship, and then AH-NI-GHI´-TO'S father said they must not tarry longer, for already the new ice was beginning to form in the bay, and in a short time it would be too thick for the ship to force her way through, and they would be obliged to spend the winter in the Snowland. As no one was prepared to do this, every one felt a little anxious until the

Winter in the Snowland

open sea was again reached. But here a new trouble awaited AH-NI-GHI'-TO and her friends; for a terrible storm arose, and the ship rolled and tossed about until it seemed as if the iron stone must surely dash through the ship's side. Of course AH-NI-GHI'-TO'S father had men watching all the time to notice the slightest change, but everything had been so securely packed that nothing moved. AH-NI-GHI'-TO was very glad

71

when at last the storm was over and the big waves calmed down, for she had had her first attack of seasickness, and did not like it at all. After the storm the weather grew milder, and AH-NI-GHI'-TO'S father told her she might visit her birthplace at the head of Bowdoin Bay, which pleased her very much. She knew the little black house where the stork had brought her had been burned, but Baby Lake and the gravel bank, the big black cliffs of Mt. Bartlett, and the great white glacier were all old friends, and AH-NI-GHI'-TO wanted to see them again. Ere the bay was reached the snow had begun to fall, and by the time AH-NI-GHI'-TO'S birthplace was reached several inches of snow covered everything. Nevertheless she was taken ashore by her father and mother, and on the spot where the little black house once stood, she brushed the snow away and picked a handful of big yellow poppies. Up on the gravel bank she dug out a few white round pebbles and then paid a visit to the little lake. Here she found three pretty ducks swimming about; but as soon as the little fur-clad

Ah-ni-ghi'-to on the Site of the Little Black House

figure appeared they flew away over the hills, and only the steep brown cliffs of the great mountain frowned down upon her, and in the distance the surface of the white glacier gleamed through the fast-falling snow.   The storm was increasing in violence, and AH-NI-GHI'-TO was hurried back to the ship.

Good-bye was said to all the Eskimos, with promises of a return some day, and the ship started for home.

This had been a very unusual summer. Much snow had fallen, and many storms took the place of the usual sunshine. The natives laid all this to the removing of the iron mountain, and told AH-NI-GHI'-TO'S father, when they bade him good-bye, that they feared they would never see him again, for they were sure the ship, with all on board, would go to the bottom of the sea.

They were very much distressed, and begged him to put the stone ashore here, and thus avoid the ill luck which would surely befall him. He tried to assure them that the ship would reach home safely, but they seemed very sad when the vessel steamed away.

For a time it seemed as if the weather had united with the evil spirit which the Eskimos had said protected the iron stones, and the wind and sea together tried their best to set free the great meteorite by pounding it through the ship's sides or turning the vessel over.

But the good ship withstood all their attacks, and finally the stormy wind became a favoring breeze and smoothed the tumbling waves into a smiling sea.

AH-NI-GHI´-TO was now bound for home, and the vessel steamed steadily toward the south, stopping at one point to take on board a party of gentlemen who had spent the summer studying the rocks and ice rivers. Still farther south, another stop was made to gather fossils. AH-NI-GHI´-TO'S father took her with him to the fossil-beds, as the scientific men called the hillside where the fossils were to be found, and showed her the flat shaly stones which when split open had pictures of leaves and twigs upon the inner surface. He told her that many, many years ago, it was always summer in this spot where now it was always winter; that the ground on which she stood was then covered with ferns and flowers instead of snow and ice; and that, just as she had seen her mother press the flowers she had gathered, in the sunny places among the rocks, between the leaves of books to preserve them that she might show them to friends at home, so these ferns and leaves of long, long ago had been pressed, by the wind and rain, between sheets of mud which have turned to stone, so that the learned men who were now opening these stone books, or fossils, with their hammers could see what kind of plants and trees grew then in this country.

After a few hours AH-NI-GHI´-TO was again on her way South; and the next stopping-place was a little town called Umanak, made up of only about a dozen habitations. There were three Danish families in this place, but in only one family were there children, and these children, five in number, had never in all their lives seen another white child before. They were delighted with AH-NI-GHI´-TO. Each one tried to do more for her than the other, and while AH-NI-GHI´-TO could not understand one word of their language and they could not understand a word of hers, yet they had a happy afternoon together. AH-NI-GHI´-TO'S toys were as new to them as their quaint and mostly home-made ones were to her. They were dear, generous, good-hearted little ones, and wanted to make AH-NI-GHI´-TO a present of everything she admired. They had funny little Eskimo dolls made of rags, and dressed just like an Eskimo girl, with long fur stockings, with the fur side next the leg, and over these, tanned sealskin boots; short sealskin trousers, with the fur on the outside, and trimmed down the front with bands of colored leather. The body was covered with a woollen blouse, shaped like one of our sweaters, and lined with eiderdown. The bottom of the blouse was trimmed with ribbon. Seaweed was used for the hair, which was tied up in a top knot with a broad piece of ribbon.

The dolls were not pretty, but very odd, and unlike any AH-NI-GHI´-TO had ever seen; and these little children were just as fond of them as AH-NI-GHI´-TO was of her beautiful bisque dolls, which have real hair and can open and shut their eyes. They insisted on giving one of their dolls to AH-NI-GHI´-TO to take home with her. AH-NI-GHI´-TO felt very proud of this gift, and said she would keep it always in remembrance of the little strangers who were so kind to her. She gave them oranges, the first they had ever seen. It was not until she had peeled one and broken it in pieces that she could make the eldest, a little boy who was about seven years old, believe it was not a ball, but a fruit, and good to eat.

When they had tasted of the orange, they could hardly wait to peel others before eating them. When AH-NI-GHI'-TO saw that they liked this new fruit, she sent them a basket full, all she had left, as soon as she returned to the ship. The Eskimos in this place brought pretty little sealskin boots and slippers decorated with bits of colored leather to AH-NI-GHI'-TO, also toy boats and sledges patterned after the large ones which they used. Laura, too, received her share of souvenirs, for she was a great curiosity, both to the Eskimos as well as the white people. Some of the natives had never even heard of colored people.

Towards evening AH-NI-GHI'-TO bade all her new friends good-bye, promising to surely visit them if she ever made the voyage to the Snowland again.

THE SNOW BABY

Ah-ni-ghi´-to on Deck

As the good ship sailed South, she gradually came into the zone where the sun goes down every evening and rises every morning. This AH-NI-GHI´-TO did not like at all, for now she could not go on deck after supper as she had been in the habit of doing, nor could she have daylight in her cabin whenever she pleased by simply pulling the old hat out of the tiny round window. Instead, she had the moon and stars to keep her company through the night.

One morning (it was the twelfth of September) AH-NI-GHI´-TO awoke and found on a little stand by the side of her bed a beautiful cake all

79

Ah-ni-ghi'-to's Birthday

iced with chocolate,——this was her favorite cake,
——and upon it four colored candles burning
brightly.   What do you suppose this meant?
It meant that four years ago that day the stork
had brought little AH-NI-GHI'-TO to her father
and mother, in the little black house way up in
the Snowland; so this was her birthday.   All the
gentlemen on board ship, whom she called her
"brothers," had remembered the little girl, and
her presents were different from any she had ever
received on her other birthdays.   There were ivory

rings, an ivory locket and chain, and an ivory cross; all these had been carved by the Eskimos. Then there were two white-fox skins, and two blue-fox skins; sealskin mittens, shoes, and slippers; a muff and neckpiece made of eiderdown, and a lovely eiderdown quilt, with the beautiful green and black skins of the necks of the birds used as a border all around it. But the funniest thing of all was a big Eskimo doll, almost as tall as AH-NI-GHI´-TO herself, dressed like an Eskimo hunter, with his sealskin trousers and coat, and his fur hood pulled over his face in true Eskimo style. Such a happy little girl she was that day. In the afternoon she invited her friends, whom she called her brothers, to share her cake and whatever else could be found in the "goody" line. What a jolly time there was in the little cabin! Every one wished AH-NI-GHI´-TO "many happy returns of the day;" the captain hoisted the stars and stripes on the mainmast, and the engineer blew four loud blasts with the whistle. This, he said, would let all the seals and walrus, and even the polar bears, if there were any within hearing distance, know that there was a celebration on board ship, and that AH-NI-GHÍ-TO, the Snow Baby, was four years old that day. If they heard the whistle, they did not make any sign, for not an animal was to be seen.

It was still a week's sailing before the American shore would be reached, and AH-NI-GHÍ-TO began to grow eager to get home, where she had left her family of dolls, taking only her eldest with her, for, she said, "they must miss a mother's care, poor things, and I am homesick for them too. I wonder what they will say to the new Eskimo sister and brother that I am bringing to them. I hope they will be pleased, even if the new children are not beauties. Then, too, I am so anxious to tell all my dear ones what a good time I have had, and to show them my new presents and also to give them the curious things I have brought from the Snowland for them."

At last the shore was in sight, and toward evening it was reached. That night AH-NI-GHÍ-TO slept in a hotel with her father and mother; and very queer it felt to sleep in a bed

Home Again

that did not rock to and fro, and to wake in the night and not hear the steady, even pulsing of the engine, together with the swish of the waves against the ship's sides, which had been her steady company for nearly three months.

There was still a long journey to be made on the railroad, and AH-NI-GHI´-TO thought it would never end.   But at last, with a clanging of bells and a puffing of steam, the long dusty train rolled into the station, and there among the eager crowd AH-NI-GHI´-TO saw her "Tante" and the gentle kindly face of "dear old Grossma,"

83

both glad to have their baby back again safe and well.

Of course there was much to hear and much to tell; presents to give, friends to see, and her own family of dolls to look after and the new ones to be introduced, until when night came it was a very tired AH-NI-GHI'-TO that mother tucked away in the little white bed.

"Good night, mother dear," she said. "I have had a very nice time, and I am glad to have seen the Snowland again, and 'Billy-Bah,' and the little brown Eskimos, and those dear little children who gave me the Eskimo doll, even if they could not speak English or German. The christening of the meteorite was great fun, and I liked the big ship and our funny little room, and I liked my big brothers on the ship; but I like Grossma's house the very best of all, don't you?"